CW00384595

OVER THE BRIDGE

Over the Bridge

Edited by John Loveday

Illustrated by Michael Foreman

Kestrel Books

KESTREL BOOKS
Published by Penguin Books Ltd
Harmondsworth, Middlesex, England

First published 1981
Published simultaneously in paperback by Puffin Books

ISBN 0 7226 5742 0

Printed in Great Britain by
Richard Clay (The Chaucer Press) Ltd,
Bungay, Suffolk

Over the Bridge

For the children of Whitchurch School, Oxfordshire, and the audiences at the poetry readings given there by the poets who have contributed to this anthology.

The village of Whitchurch is approached by a toll-bridge over the Thames. This is, in part, the bridge of the title. The book itself I have thought of as a bridge over which the young reader may cross into the 'landscape' of poetry.

J.L.

Acknowledgements

The editor wishes to express gratitude to the following for practical encouragement in the early stages of the creation of the anthology. Mr and Mrs B. Aburrow, Mr and Mrs C. Aldridge, Mr and Mrs P. Bagley, Mr and Mrs P. Hawley, Mr and Mrs J. Holmes, Mr F. Makepiece, Mr P. Mottley, Dr B. Newport, Mr and Mrs E. Osers, Gwen Robinson, Mr F. Sedgwick, Cholsey Junior School, The National Poetry Secretariat, The Southern Arts Association.

Contents

7

'I'D HEARD THE STORY'

'BY RUNGS OR SHAFTS OF RHYME'

Introduction

Many years ago, I saw a photograph of a crowd of soldiers on a hillside during the Spanish Civil War. Though the details are now unclear in memory, the impression of that picture remains. The attention of all those men was turned towards one man – a poet, reading his work to them.

The distance from that Spanish hillside to the hall of an English primary school is not only a matter of miles; but when, in the early nineteen-seventies, I began to invite poets to come to a small village school in Oxfordshire to read their poems to adult audiences, it was with a certainty that poetry should be good enough for the ordinary interested person to listen to, as those soldiers listened. It should draw us from our common concerns and hold our attention for a while with its meaning and feeling, its forcefulness or charm, and sometimes follow us when we have gone on our way.

Perhaps some of the soldiers carried that poet's words with them, towards whatever lay ahead.

In ten years, over thirty-five poets have read at Whitchurch, some on several occasions. The audiences have been quite large, usually about a hundred people, many travelling long distances. A few have had a particular interest in poetry; a few have been poets themselves; most have simply been people ready to listen because the poetry was good enough to listen to.

But these have been evening events, nothing to do with the day-time life of the school. I thought one day that, perhaps, a connection could be made, and asked the poets if they might be interested in contributing poems to a book for the children. At first, the idea was to make a small privately-printed book, and with the generosity of some members of the audience at the readings, and the efforts of a group of pupils, it was possible to offer a small fee. 'I'd be delighted to be a contributor to such an

9

anthology,' wrote one poet. 'The whole idea sounds immensely attractive.' His words may stand for them all. It quickly became clear that the book might deserve more than a local readership, and I began to collect the poems with a book such as the anthology has now become in mind. After a year, and with half of the poems in an exciting folder on my desk, I wrote to the publishers to explore their possible interest. The reply was encouraging, and the collection continued with increased purposefulness.

It was necessary to be patient, to wait for real poems to occur, in the strange, unforced way that such poems do. The collecting took two years, but here now is the book, full of the life and newness of writing unseen, unread before. I believe that most of these poems will not lose their vitality and freshness with the passing of time.

They are poems to grow with. I asked for poems that might be enjoyed by some young readers of ten or eleven years and yet were likely, later, to be included in books for adults. One of the first poets invited, Vernon Scannell, quoted in his reply some words of W. H. Auden. They seemed so true that I, in turn, quoted them in my letters to the other poets. '. . . *While there are some good poems that are only for adults, because they presuppose adult experience in their readers, there are no good poems which are only for children.*'

Most of the poets wrote specially for this book; others let me see their current work, in case it contained something suitable. One poem, Charles Tomlinson's 'The Littleton Whale', I liked so much when the poet read it to an audience at the Poetry Centre in London that I asked if its first printing in book form could be in *Over the Bridge*. If a poem did not quite suit the pattern of the book, the writer might agree to try again. Some poets contributed more than one poem, when I suggested that companion-pieces would be pleasing. All agree with my concern that the craft they love should not seem, to a new generation of readers, merely a lesson subject.

It seemed right that the children at Whitchurch should become familiar with at least some of 'their' poems before they became a book for others to share. They even helped, to a small extent, with advice when I was not sure whether a particular poem should be included. In this way, 'In Cimino's *The Deer Hunter*', by D. M. Thomas, a topical poem I was afraid might not be appreciated, because it is based on an X-Certificate film the children might never see, was firmly voted 'in'. Could they guess who Cimino might be? I wondered. Would they know about the 'playing' of Russian roulette? I need not have worried. Their guesses about Cimino (the director of the film) were intelligent; and on Russian roulette they were theoretical experts. But what caught their sympathetic imaginations most strongly was the image of the eyes of the shot deer.

This leads to an important point. Nowhere does D. M. Thomas mention his feelings for the deer, and yet, powerfully, feeling is conveyed. What is true in this instance is character-istic of the book as a whole. '*Poetry presents the thing in order to convey the feeling*,' wrote Wei T'ai, nine hundred years ago. '*It should be precise about the thing and reticent about the feeling, for as soon as the mind responds and connects with the thing the feeling shows in the words; this is how poetry enters deeply into us.*' So, whether in the instance of the shot deer's eyes, or Charles Tomlinson's pig's head, James Simmons's old uncle, Ted Walker's midnight music, Roger Garfitt's dog, or any of the other images in these pages, the poet's feelings are shown, and ours aroused, through the precise and vivid presentation of *things*.

The poems are arranged in three sections. The first contains those that derive from the writer's direct experience, ranging from memories of childhood to thoughts of death. The second is a group of 'fictions' and other tales: legends, fables, invented portraits. The final section presents poems in which some aspect of poetic technique seems of predominant interest: the use of a set form, the sustaining of a rhyme. In at least two instances, poems might almost equally well have been placed in different sections. 'In the Land of Cockayne', by Iain Crichton Smith, based on a well-known painting by Breugel, might be considered a fiction, but I have preferred to think of it as a presentation of the writer's experience, his experience of a painting. Gavin

I I

Ewart's 'The Quarrel' is obviously related to experience, and could be placed in the first section, but the clever and amusing rhymings were undoubtedly central to the writer's concern, and so determined its placing in section three.

Somewhere there are readers who have taken this book from a shelf with curiosity and an expectation of pleasure. If you are one of them, the book is made for you. I hope that you may find here 'voices' worth listening to.

J.L.

This Book

This book is a bridge. You cross alone.
The landscape entered is your own:

a waking song; a boy's shadow;
a voice from the dead; a plane down low

as the war begins; a face in a well,
a floating rat; a cat's cradle;

a cat bewitched; a staring stoat,
a screeching hare; a girl's spread coat

on a lonely path; the upturned snout
of a running pig; the eyes cut out

from a dead pig's head; dead soldiers' eyes,
the eyes of a deer; a hurt moth's cries;

cascading light in a French garden;
dead Jill's friends remembering;

old Davy lost, with Olive gone;
a tree's last leaves still hanging on;

a moonlit night from long ago;
music outside a Spanish window;

a Redskin boy imagining
a girl unclothed; a seal shedding

her sealskin for a human form
a fisherman captures and takes home;

a peacock stripped stark naked by
a man from Mars; a swamp gone dry

where mud-fish live (a poet's brain
makes fabled sense of mud and rain);

a boy who flies, birdlike; three cats
in clever rhyme; a cricket leap-

ing lines, like this; a couple shouting, swearing; fat Aunt Flo', without

her underwear; old Itzig's dog
who wags his tail for Itzig's god;

a lurcher, Blue, who ran and slipped
his leash in bleached-out grass and leapt

in here; bloodhounds, a running man;
a tiger, caged; a veteran

of tall ship days, his sailor's tale
of times long gone; a stranded whale

in Gloucestershire, 68 feet long;
a walk in Spain; a woodman's song;

Anne's cat that eats a rabbit's 'jewels'
(poetic word for testicles);

a cold fish, and his end; the sound
of Sunday t.v., underground

in a dead man's ears; and, last, a small
Knock Knock – Who's there? on door or wall:

The landscape entered is your own.
This book is a bridge. You cross alone.

JOHN LOVEDAY

'ENTER THE REAL WORLD'

Waking Song

Enter the poor struggle
Of birdsong
Weakly cheering the dawn.

Enter the first light
Like a feeble lamp
Through the orange blind.

Enter the real world
With a shove of grey shoulders
Into my bed of dreams.

Enter the rousing tin-can
Crash of the postman
With his red salute.

Enter the sweet female
With kindness caught in a cup
And the letter from you.

Enter the rapid twirl
Of young life and its skirts
Signing with black ink on the quilt.

And the morning begins.

PHILIP CALLOW

I Would Run with My Shadow

I would run with my shadow, watch him jumping
up at me round a post, peeling himself round
railings. Sometimes he'd wriggle freely, bumping
over stones without hurting himself; sometimes
he was forced to stay bowed, stiffly bent, bound
at a wall. With my hands, amazed at his mimes,
I'd be rabbit or wolf. The sunrise would stretch
him to a giant and the noon to a blot. At sunset
he would hide and be lost. Then a switch would fetch
him back. Tables and chairs chopped his silhouette
into pieces. A fire was best. He would gad
about over the world as if he were mad.

EDMOND LEO WRIGHT

Once a Stone Was a Car

Once a stone was a car. It only need be
roughly square at the edges: that was enough
if it fitted the fingers to let me see
me as driver at Brooklands on the banking
made of air. At eleven I couldn't bluff
myself thus: then there had to be wheels flanking
a neat chassis – they needn't go round as long
as they showed all their spokes. Later they had to –
plus a helmeted driver – couldn't be wrong
that I only had half of him. Wouldn't do
at fifteen without scale-model Jaguars.
Wouldn't do at eighteen to take stones for cars.

EDMOND LEO WRIGHT

You Put Knobs on a Board

You put knobs on a board which had holes in it.
You could make any picture you liked: the cat
(though his whiskers were thick and didn't quite fit)
and the house (though the door would always
    stay shut)
with its smoke from the chimney (but only flat
lines and upright to show where the grime and smut
could go). Flowers in place by the garden wall
had no smell and no petals. Octagonal tyres
made the car ride a bumpy one, and a ball
had to have lots of corners. Pictures were liars,
I thought, but it was not as I had supposed:
you can see them all right with your eyes half closed.

EDMOND LEO WRIGHT

Bournemouth: September 3rd, 1939

My summer ends, and term begins next week.
Why am I here in Bournemouth, with my aunt
And 'Uncle Bill', who something tells me can't
Be really my uncle? People speak
In hushed, excited tones. Down on the beach
An aeroplane comes in low over the sea
And there's a scattering as people reach
For towels and picnic gear and books, and flee
Towards the esplanade. Back at the hotel
We hear what the Prime Minister has said.
'So it's begun.' 'Yes, it was bound to.' 'Well,
Give it till Christmas.' Later, tucked in bed,
I hear the safe sea roll and wipe away
The castles I had built in sand that day.

ANTHONY THWAITE

Aunt Flo'

Was like a dumpling on legs, with a face as gentle
With colour and wrinkles as a stored pippin,
Her flesh rich and as yeasty as fresh bread.
When she served dinner we would all rush
For the far end of the long table,
The plates passed down as she overwhelmed them
With potatoes, meat, gravy and greens
Until the dishes and tureens were empty.
'Oh dear,' she would say to those who sat near her,
'There's none left for you!'
Then the ritual was to be sent to the kitchen for
    cheese
And a cottage loaf which prompted me to wonder
Did the baker use her as a model?

Strictly teetotal, she sustained her abstinence
On Wincarnis and home-made wines.
'It's good for you,' she would say
To nephews and nieces, 'it's natural.'
While mothers winced to see their young ones
    reeling away,
And her more sophisticated daughters
Recoiled at her too obvious refusal
To wear underclothes in warm weather.

Delectably dotty, Aunt Flo'
Blundered beautifully through life
And taught us, when, later,
In despair of making sense of things,
That it didn't matter.

JOHN COTTON

The Séance

To speak with the dead:
Now there was an idea of wonder and profundity!
My parents, when on holiday
Near Blackgang Chine, had met a medium,
Together with a man whose one desire
Was to contact a loved and long dead brother.
The idea took fire,
My eight years' mind worked overtime
On what the adults aimed to do.
If it were true,
What could we ask him? Learn?

The séance planned,
The solemn nature of it stressed,
All seriousness, I looking on,
They linked their hands and minds in concentration.
The voice, when it came, sounded distressed,
Unmasculine, quite odd:
But from another world, what to expect?
'Are you there?' the medium asked.
'Yes,' it said and sounded very sad.
'Something is worrying you, is something bad?'
'Yes,' the spirit said again.
Now for it, I thought, and could hear
The others holding breath.
Then very clear:
'He is wearing *my* shirt.'
And that still worried after death?

'It's true! It's true!'
The living brother cried,
'Only he could have known,
I took it when he died.'
'I'm afraid you've startled him:
He's growing faint,' the medium said.
'Oh yes – he's gone.'

So that was it.
The brother satisfied paid out his guineas,
The other adults impressed,
Stunned in their surprise;
While I held on to the unspoken: 'Is that all?'
And to the lasting lesson,
There's no end to what they'll trivialize.

JOHN COTTON

The Well

'You'll never bring him up, my dear:
That vein across his little nose –
A sign he'll drown.'
                              The coverlet,
The pillow, and the small face blurred.
She held the handle hard, the pram
Her only anchor in a world
In flood. 'I'm sorry, dear, to tell
You this, but that's a sign.'
                              Then she
Was walking home, old Biah gone,
Her crow's garb gone, her white face gone,
Her words not gone, never to go.

You dropped a stone in, and the sound
Came up a long time afterwards,
A cold sound, dark, that frightened you
To make you look and drop again.
Lean over far enough, and far,
Far down, a face looked up at you.
You broke it with a stone.

The pail went lolloping down, banging
The dark green sides, until it tipped
And sank. You wound it up slowly,
Not to spill. There was another way.

Let go, the iron handle spun,
The chain raced off the roller and
The pail fell straight. After the jerk,
The chain was tight, down there the pail
Suspended still. Winding, you looked
For its coming back, the glimmering
About to break the surface, felt
Something like welcome for it when
It spilt its silver round the rim.

How long is 'bringing up'? she wondered
As the years passed, watched the vein,
Less noticeable as boyhood came.
Was there a time beyond which all
Harm's ways were barred? the pond outside
The door, the well, the summer sea,
And all the unknown places dared
In urchin hours? Tom scoffed, but built
A wooden structure on the well,
With bolted door. 'These bloody old
Wives' tales.' But some were sometimes true.

In time, the bolt stayed drawn, the door
Even lay open carelessly.
(Once, a rat was found, floating,
The water left untouched for days.)
The curious stones dropped in, and soon
The pail, wound on a chain of trust
In what was normal for a boy –
Who did not drown.

Disused for years,
The well has been filled in, rubble
And soil have proved it shallower
Than a boy's imaginings.
He'll not drown here.

The vein still shows,
The more when tension comes, though five
Decades have gone. He wonders sometimes if
Old Biah had the superstition wrong,
If some dark water waits him still.
The hand that held the pram will never know.

JOHN LOVEDAY

Cat's Cradle

(For Tim)

A cradle made of string
   For hands to ply and plait,
Teasing a see-saw thread
   For one old journeying cat.

We swung him down the night,
   Mewed in his wicker ark;
His dancing eyes lit up
   The soundless dews and dark.

Summers of goose-grass led
   Down paths we had not made
To nests of tabby gloom,
   Soft play of sun and shade.

Long absence held our breaths;
   The house grew wide and bare
Until he called us home.
   I cut out of cold air

His face with its sharp look,
   His fur grown stray and dim –
For these long miles of sleep,
   Let the earth cradle him.

PETER SCUPHAM

Amber

I think that the tortoise-shell cat
Who lives with my aunt
Is a bewitched thing:
By no means, wholly, only, cat.
She's a shape-shifter, a body-changer,
Who in turn has been
Phoenix, mermaid, hippogriff.
Through feather and skin and scale
Her slit green eyes have seen
Glass mountains, emerald caves,
And the outer rims of space.
For this stately, crazy puss
Now roams for hours
On the soft South Downs,
In sheep's form, owl's plumes,
Under snail's shell, moth's wings.
My aunt calls her back
With a clack of her scissors.
Then quickly in cat's skin,
Amber runs home
To play with string, purr with fire,
If they're alone.
Crouched in anger and fear,
She hides when I'm there.
Aunt says she hates strangers.

SHIRLEY TOULSON

32

Blue

Memory on a peg
behind the door:

the slip-leash a live line
through my fingers

that floats on his shoulders'
running water

or knows their stiffening
the undertow

of another presence
in the hedgebank

still rancorous with fox.
Always that shock

as the hackles rise on
a waking dream,

an ancient line stands out
in the young dog.

Slip him, and I become
the outer ear,

the iris of his eye,
ready to shout

if he conjures a fox
as he stag-leaps

and salmons the long grass.
Enter the land

within the land, a light
and shadow land

whose denizens are quick
and changing shapes,

where the pheasant's wing spreads
into dead wood,

and riddles of brown earth
in the stubble

or clods of bleached-out grass
in the furrow

soon as our backs are turned
go haring off.

Enter the light and dark
of the duel,

the dog's dive and dolphin
over the ground,

a shoulder gleam breaking
the air's surface,

a slate gleam, night closing
with each new stride,

the hare's running rings, her
lucky numbers,

noughts and figures of eight
a breathing space

won on every turn.
Enter the dark

of that other duel
he fought, the leash

an allegiance he held,
a last life line.

Sorrow still rives me that
I let him slip.

ROGER GARFITT

Your Own Way

A Kerry Story

I heard this sound one night,
A class of wild screeching!
What in the name of God's that,
Says I, rolling down the bedclothes.

Down with me through the kitchen
And out into the empty barnyard,
Big bare feet in the moonlight.
A hare I saw, on top of the turf

With a stoat staring at it,
And the hare squealing, on and on
Like a certified madwoman;
It would lift your head off!

I took it by the two ears,
As long and warm as gloves,
And dropped it inside the door,
Then back to the cold bed.

Round and round then, *hopping*.
Nothing seemed to stop it,
Bumping through the kitchen,
And with every bump, a break.

Not a wink of sleep did I get
Till near dawn, when I raced
Down again, for the second time,
And fired it out the doorway

37

Past the still waiting stoat.
There was silence after that!
You'll probably say I was cruel,
But there was no way round it.

It was between me and the beast,
And whether it was a faery woman
Or just a daft hare and a stoat,
It's your own way you must do it.

JOHN MONTAGUE

In the Land of Cockayne

In the Land of Cockayne
the peasant sleeps on his flail
and his shirt is a white cloud
that is lying becalmed.

In the Land of Cockayne
the little round pig waddles along
with his snout curved upward
and a knife in his side.

In the Land of Cockayne
there is a headless egg with legs
and inside it where the yolk should be
is a wooden-handled spoon.

In the Land of Cockayne
a young man spread-legged is staring at the sky
his head resting on a black cloak
and a Bible beside him.

In the Land of Cockayne
the trees have fresh green leaves
and there are boats like tureens on the lochs
loaded with pheasants.

In the Land of Cockayne
a pair of false teeth are waiting
for the taste of roast beef
for the passing bounty of wine.

IAIN CRICHTON SMITH

Giving Rabbit to My Cat Bonnie

Pretty Bonnie, you are as quick as a rabbit,
though your tail's longer,
emphasizing suppressed disapproval,
and your ears are shorter – two
radar detectors set on swivels
either side of your skull, and your yawn
is a view of distant white spires – not
the graveyard jaw of this poor dead naked pink

rabbit, who, like you, was a
technological success, inheriting a snazzy
fur coat, pepper-and-salt coloured, cosy,
and beautiful fur shoes with spiked toes.
You're both of you
better dressed than I am for most occasions.
Take off your shoes and suits, though,
what have you got?

Look puss, I've brought us a rabbit for supper.
I bought it in a shop.
The butcher was haggis-shaped, ham-coloured,
not a bit like you. His ears
were two fungi on the slab of his head.
He had a fat, flat face.
But he took your brother rabbit off a hook
and spread him on the counter like a rug,

and slice, slice, scarcely looking,
pulled the lovely skin off like a bag.
So, Bonnie, all I've brought us is food
in this silly pink shape – more like me, really.
I'll make a wine sauce with mushrooms, but will
you want this precious broken heart? this perfect liver?
See, protected in these back pockets – jewels!
Bonnie, what are you eating? Dear Bonnie, consider!

ANNE STEVENSON

On a Pig's Head

Once it had gorged itself
to a pitch of succulence, they slew it:
it was the stare in the eyes
the butcher hated, and so removed
with a quick knife,
transforming the thing
to a still life, hacked
and halved, cross-cutting it
into angles with ears.
It bled no more,
though the black pearls
still lurked on its rawness.
The ears were streaked with wax,
the teeth stained near the roots
like an inveterate smoker's.
It was the nose looked freshest –
a rubbery, soft pink.
With a spill of paper, I cleaned
the orifice of each ear,
and played water into the nostrils.
The brain was a mere thimble of brain,
and the tongue, smaller than a sheep's
sliced neatly. The severed ears
seemed delicate on their plate
with their maze of veins.
When we submerged it in brine
to change it to brawn and galantine,
it wouldn't fit the bowls:
evidently, it had been conceived

for a more capacious age.
Divided, it remained massive
leaving no room for reflection
save that peppercorns, cloves
of garlic, bay-leaves and wine
would be necessary for its transformation.
When set to boil, it required
a rock, a great
red one
from Macuilxochitl
to keep it down.

CHARLES TOMLINSON

In Cimino's *The Deer Hunter*

In Cimino's *The Deer Hunter*
the captured Americans
are forced to play Russian roulette.
I am fascinated by
the convincing – but quite small –
change in their expression
when they lose.

Of course they are only acting.
The eyes of the shot deer
earlier in the film
glaze, and slide, no more
convincingly yet somehow
with more conviction,
because the deer is not acting.

D. M. THOMAS

Moth

Filling a jug with hot water
I saw a black flutter,
saw something leap.
A moth danced on the scalding water.
In my childhood I tore wings off flies.
Now I can hear the screams of scalded moths.

D. M. THOMAS

Woodman's Song

Heather, bracken, whortleberry fail.
My solitude is like this patch
Of stones, set randomly together
Against the encroachment of gentle grass,
   And without use or change.

Dew knits its web across the turf,
Deepens the colour of rotting leaves
By the path, eases the earth to mud.
No colour deepens across the stones,
   No weather blunts their edge.

Mightn't my solitude be the pool
Where at dusk deer come to drink,
Slotting the border with their hooves;
From where the stag's uncomforted bellow
   Carries when night has fallen?

Mightn't my solitude be these larch trees,
Leaning, derelict, on one another?
Mightn't it be the wind-torn ash
That spreads above a grove of seedlings
   And its own tumbled limbs?

Mightn't the presence of these things,
Dewy, intensifying to a glitter,
Image the humanness of my body?
Couldn't I keep this light within me,
    Precarious and unspilled?

Heather, bracken, whortleberry fail.
My solitude is like this patch
Of stones, set randomly together
Against the encroachment of gentle grass,
    And without use or change.

Robert Wells

Around Sheepwash

Walking along these lanes again,
counting the trees in the hedgerows – hazel,
willow, bramble, honeysuckle, oak
(still leafless this, but the cork marbles
betrayed it), blackthorn in smudgy flower,
and the holly and the ivy – the carol came
irresistibly – I passed these things:
a black and white goose, cosy-catlike
on a cottage doorstep (I stared and smiled);
a half-grown puppy (I played solemn,
sent it sternly home); two lambs
loose outside a gate with a gap
(I tiptoed past, not to frighten them,
leaving their mothers to baa them back);
a thatched barn deep in a hollow
at a curve in the lane, its door furry
with the dangling tails of slaughtered vermin
(I puzzled over them, teasing after
the shapes of the bodies that had borne them);
then slow solitudes of hawk and cloud,
wind in thickets, the sun westering;
and half a mile before the village,
near the river, on the roadside verge,
a girl's coat, well-made, slim-waisted,
spread on its back, sleeves tidy,
primroses tucked into one pocket;
stark empty. And I hastened my steps.

FLEUR ADCOCK

Paper Windmills

'Molinos de Papel? There's nothing there,'
She said, and slapped my change down on the bar.
In my mind's eye I saw the summer air
Troubling some paper windmills. 'Is it far?'

I asked, 'I'd like to go.' She tossed her hair
In disbelief and scorn. 'You have a car?'
'Well, no,' I said. 'I'll walk. The day is fair.'
So I trod two hours through the melting tar,

Found nothing but deserted pulping mills –
If nothing may include a house or two
With foaming roses at the window sills

Above a patio where a couple sat.
White petals filled with wind. Nothing to do
But leave, I watched some fall, settled for that.

TED WALKER

(Author's note: *molinos* is Spanish for 'mills' and *papel* for 'paper'.)

St Paul-de-Vence

Assis dans le jardin, tous trois,
De corps et d'esprit séparés,
Chacun songeait,
Certain,
Seul,
Avec ses secrètes pensées.

Mireille, palette en main, de nuances plus
    tendres rêvait,
Alexandre, de maçonnerie, de vitrage, de
    charpente, et d'acier,
Guillaume de mots nombreux les pages de son
    cahier couvrait.

Au silence personne ne parlait,
Personne les dates ne comptait.

Sur eux
Rayons de soleil mettaient
Des reflets d'or.

Un vent les caressait,
Murmurant, chantant, berçant.

Le chien, lui, à l'ombre,
Dans son sommeil
Une plainte poussant
De pistes à jamais perdues se souvenait.

Tout près
Le mas provençal
Se repose
Plein d'une cargaison
De livres
De tableaux
De musique
De fruits.

Au silence personne ne parlait,
Personne les dates ne comptait.

A. L. HENDRIKS

St Paul-de-Vence

They sat in the garden, separate,
Each with secure, clear thought.

Mireille holding her palette
Dreaming of subtler tints,
Alex visioning timber
And steel and concrete and glass,
Guillaume putting on paper
Words upon words upon words.

Nobody spoke to the silence,
No one mentioned the date.

The sun cascaded,
Drenching their figures with light,
And the wind moved like a dancer,
Sinuous, confident, strong.

The dog asleep in the shadow,
Moaned in his dream,
Following scents lost forever;

And behind,
The Provençal house
Sprawled
With a cargo of books
And pictures
And music
And fruit.

Nobody spoke to the silence,
No one mentioned the date.

A. L. HENDRIKS

(Author's note: I am greatly indebted to my mother, Simone
Lemière Hendriks, for invaluable assistance and advice in the
composition of the French version.)

Jill's Death

After Jill died they remembered how she liked this chair,
her jokes about an ornament in the corner.
They did not trek mournfully to the cemetery
with its array of crosses at the border of the town.
They called some flowerbeds in the garden Jill's beds
and said 'How are Jill's flowers today?' and went
outside and looked at them. The flowers swayed
or hardly moved in the slight wind. This
perfection spoke of the exact nature of life
with undismayed joyfulness.

GEORGE BUCHANAN

Olive and Davy

When conversation failed
the family album came down.
A portrait of Aunt Olive
in her B.A. gown

stunned me, hair sculpted
neatly round her ears,
so beautiful I stole it
and had it for years.

When age and her last illness
ravaged her face
the gold hair still shone
with all its old grace.

I remembered it last night
when Uncle Davy died.
Was that why he wanted
no one at his side

this last year, a widower?
We knew he'd seen more
of the wide world than most of us,
Australia, Samoa,

Nigeria; but not much,
we presumed, of life,
him with his speech defect
and his lovely wife.

Uncle Davy, very quiet,
and Olive, my aunt
so strikingly beautiful,
so gay and so fluent

his one rebuke in public
echoed like a riot,
telling his back-seat driver,
'Olive, be quiet.'

The winter she died
he brought sweets and sherry
to my mother's bridge evenings
and got mildly merry.

We hardly broached his bottle;
but always next time
he brought the same parcel,
courteous and kind.

Suddenly, it seemed, he grew
impatient for death,
and symptoms followed, pallor,
shortness of breath,

a new, old man, Davy,
blank, impolite,
preferring no company
night after night

to neighbourly solicitude,
an idle rout
trying to perk him up,
eking him out.

He died. This is an old story
from the common stock:
an old crock longing
for another old crock,

longing on beyond youth,
beyond beauty's decay,
beyond the grave – so it seems –
for Olive, Davy.

JAMES SIMMONS

Neighbours

Father lies across the road,
On Sundays they take flowers,
And place them in the grave vase,
Most carefully, one by one:
The old, old woman and her empty son.

In their best clothes for Sunday,
They step back home for tea,
Then turn the telly louder,
As if they wished to share
The sound, if not the picture,
With the dead man over there.

SHIRLEY TOULSON

A Fall

Their veins were white
But they still hung on with their skins.
Their skins were dry,
But they still flapped back at the wind,
'Just one more day. Just one more day.'

Then, very quietly, Monday night,
A frost-gun shot them away.
Imagine the whole population of Heaven
– Heaven was the name of the tree –
Falling down simultaneously

Dazzling the root in its bed.
'What a beautiful star,' Heaven said –
Or might have if Heaven had noticed
The difference it makes to the ground
To be thatched with ghosts.

ANNE STEVENSON

Thon Nicht

D'ye mind thon nicht?
Thon nicht langsyne
in the winter o our bairnheid?
When the muckle mune
flourished wi splendour
in the naked silence o a star-thrang lift
and the snaw
blintered doucely on ilka step and stane?

Hou strang was the warld thon nicht!
Hou grand! The shairpenin cauld
set aa our landscapes straight
in a richt perspective. The clear sicht
we got frae the wind-purged dark
shed a fresh licht on the thrawn horizon
o our raw, unsiccar dreams.

Gin ony chiel had tellt us then
o aa the ferlies and the failures
that we'd yet to face
we'd lauched – and gin we'd guessed wirsels
wad we hae kent thon nicht
thon bonnie, bonnie nicht
when eternity leamed in the nearhand dawn?

DONALD CAMPBELL

That Night

Remember that night?
That night long ago
in the last days of our childhood?
When the mighty moon
flourished in splendour
beneath the bare peace of a star-busy sky
and the snow
glittered neatly on every standing stone?

What power had the world that night!
What grace! The sharpening cold
put all our landscapes right,
had a rich perspective. The clear sight
that came from the wind-purged dark
shed a fresh light on the gauche horizon
of our rough, uncertain dreams.

If anyone had told us then
of all the magic and mischief
that still lay before us
we would have laughed – and yet
if we had guessed ourselves
would we have known that night
that lovely, lovely night
when eternity flashed in the oncoming dawn?

DONALD CAMPBELL

May Music in Castille

Below in the street, the music began
Of voices, mandolin, accordion, guitar,
That every midnight celebrate the May.
I was in bed, too sleepy by far
Yet again to listen to the minstrels play
Upon sweet mandolin, accordion, guitar,
So my eyelids closed as the melody ran.

But when the music stopped in mid-beat,
Voices and mandolin, accordion, guitar,
And the dumb-struck minstrels went their way,
And in the sky was no summer star
But storm and thunder to see out the May
And the voices, mandolin, accordion, guitar,
I rose for the rain. It strums in the street.

TED WALKER

'I'D HEARD THE STORY'

The Bad Boy of the North West Coast

Before the grown-ups awake	– haaya
and the wind blows out the stars	– haaya
I'll rise and escape from home	– haaya
I'll take clubs for the salmon	– haaya
carved hooks for the halibut	– haaya
I'll paddle the great canoe	– haaya
At home they'll cry they'll miss me	– haaya
I'll hunt for big-breasted girls	– haaya
I'll give them boiled coloured sweets	– haaya
and bracelets carved of goat horn	– haaya
When I'm tall I'll bring them home	– haaya
Then all my leering uncles	– haaya
will wear their hats of spruce root	– haaya
will drum and shake their rattles	– haaya
but I'll thrash each one of them	– haaya
I'll tear off my father's headdress	– haaya
I'll marry two girls at once	– haaya
The smaller of the darlings	– haaya
I'll dress in spotted sealskins	– haaya
and earrings of abalone shell	– haaya
The other with bigger breasts	– haaya
shan't wear anything at all	– haaya

DANNIE ABSE

(Source: *Literature of the American Indian*)

Kopakona – Seal-Woman

A Faroese Legend

I'd heard the story that they come ashore
  On the Twelfth Night,
And that year I was standing by the door
Looking into the dark; I wanted a sight
Of new year stars that might be shining out
From the deep winter sky that hid the world
Of mountain, valley, stream and lake and sea.
When dark moved against dark I had no doubt
That they had come; my hand behind me pulled
The door closed. I knew they could not see me.

Down by the shore, a low form, then another,
  Out of the sea
They came, a group of ten or twelve, closer,
On to the grass above the rocks. I could see
Round heads, soft eyes and mournful colonel whiskers
In the window's glow. The sheen of their black skin
Polished curves in the dark. Then suddenly
From each shape a new form stepped, white fires
Flowed up to my shoulder's height, moved in
To a circle of figures dancing on two limbs, free.

As they danced they sang a wild song,
  Aeolian harps
Telling of winds and caves and lives that belong
To the water world of calms and storms and deeps.
I followed as they moved away and saw

Left on the grass black shadows, their cast-off skins.
Moved by desire I took one up and stole
Into my house with it, locked in a drawer
An identity, feeling as one who wins
A prize from another world that will make him whole.

The dance was ending, they were coming near.
   Back to the shore,
Resuming their fluid forms for the rest of the year.
One who stayed searching, still human-limbed,
   was more
Lithe than all the rest, I had captured the queen.
Sure of her now I waited until she fell
Grieving and pleading to the black rocks, the hard
Merciless ground that offered only the green
Brief growth of the grass, the sweet dusty hay,
And the stubborn soil that took life and death
   from the seed.

But as man my hands could offer her my life –
   In exchange for hers:
I went to her, wrapped her in wool, a wife
Drawn from the sea. I would give her furs,
Fish in abundance, milk, bread and a fire
That would never be slaked while she graced my house
With her beauty and her body's bounty. Her eyes
In one deep glance understood my desire,
Accepted her plight, followed me into the place
She was to fill with duties and children and days.

Years passed and I had forgotten the life of the sea,
   Kopakona's world –
Everyone knew her a human wife to me,
She had few friends, the children kept her time filled.

Sometimes, coming in, I would see her gazing out
Over the sea, a dream in her face that was strange
To me. But I did not think that she grieved.
I forgot to lock the drawer, having no doubt
That she was content. Did not know she would change
Her life with me for the sea-life for which she starved.

I was bitter. No better than eel or lemming, I swore
    She had gone
Blindly following instinct, nothing more,
None of the human love and laws I'd shown
Her had lodged in her animal brain. I took
A village woman to care for the children she left
And tried to ignore my heart that spoke of the theft
Of a life's identity, of imposing a thick
Thatch of imprisonment on the weft
Of another's spirit. But once, when I had wept

Alone at night she spoke to me in sleep:
    'If you loved
Me and the years I gave, care to keep
Some tenderness of memory, see they are saved,
My kin here now, from the seal-hunters' knives.'
I woke late, heavy-eyed, went to the boats,
But the hunters had gone early out to the caves
Where the seals sheltered. When I came there the cries
Of killers and killed were silent, blood from slit throats
Crimsoned the sea. The voices of waves,

The seabird's howl, the bitter lamenting wind,
    All accused me.
The hunters called me, showed me a strange find,
A golden chain hung with a twisted key
They had taken from a she-seal's neck, the last

That they had killed. 'Such eyes the creature had,
You could almost think it human. Well, home again.
Gale-warning today.' I followed slowly, lost
Was my hope of freeing one who had once
  followed me,
Even in death bound by my golden chain.

ANNE BORN

The Littleton Whale

In memory of Charles Olson

This poem is in the form of a letter from Charles Tomlinson of Gloucestershire, England, to Charles Olson of Gloucestershire, Massachusetts, who had written to ask for information about the River Severn.

What you wrote to know
was whether
the old ship canal
still paralleled the river
south
of Gloucester (England) . . .

What I never told
in my reply
was of the morning
on that same stretch
(it was a cold
January day in '85)
when Isobel Durnell
saw the whale . . .

She was up at dawn
to get her man off on time
to the brickyard and
humping over the banks
beyond Bunny Row
a slate-grey hill showed
that the night before
had not been there . . .

73

They both ran outside
and down to the shore:
the wind was blowing
as it always blows
so hard that the tide
comes creeping up under it
often unheard . . .

The great grey-blue thing
had an eye
that watched wearily
their miniature motions as they
debated its fate
for the tide
was already feeling beneath it
floating it away . . .

It was Moses White
master mariner
owner of the sloop *Matilda*
who said the thing to do
was to get chains and a traction engine
– they got two from Olveston –
and drag it ashore:
the thing was a gift:
before long it would be
drifting off to another part of the coast
and lost to them
if they didn't move now . . .

And so the whale –
flukes, flesh, tail
trembling no longer
with a failing life –

was chained and hauled
installed above the tideline . . .

And the crowds came
to where it lay
upside down
displaying a
belly evenly-wrinkled
its eye lost to view
mouth skewed and opening into
an interior of tongue and giant sieves
that had once
filtered that diet of shrimp
its deep-sea sonar
had hunted out for it
by listening to submarine echoes
too slight
for electronic selection . . .

And Hector Knapp
wrote in his diary:
Thear was a whal
cum ashore at Littleton Pill
and bid thear a fortnight
He was sixty eaight feet long
His mouth was twelve feet
The Queen claim it at last
and sould it for forty pound
Thear supposed to be
forty thousen pepeal to see it
from all parts of the cuntry . . .

The Methodist preacher
said that George Sindry

who was a very religious man
told himself when that whale came in
he'd heard so many arguments
about the tale of Jonah not being true
that he went to Littleton to
'satisfy people'. He was a tall man
a six footer
'but I got into that whale's mouth' he said
'and I stood in it
upright . . .'

The carcass
had overstayed its welcome
so they sent up a sizeable boat
to tow it to Bristol
and put it on show there
before they cut the thing down stinking
to be sold
and spread for manure . . .

You can still see the sign
to Whale Wharf as they renamed it
and Wintle's Brickworks became
the Whale Brick
Tile and Pottery Works . . .

Walking daily onto
the now-gone premises
through the 'pasture land
with valuable deposits of clay underneath'
when the machine- and drying sheds
the five kilns, the stores and stables
stood permanent in that place
of their disappearance

Enoch Durnell still
relished his part in all that history begun
when Bella shook
and woke him with a tale that the tide
had washed up a whole house
with blue slates on it into Littleton Pill
and that house was a whale . . .

CHARLES TOMLINSON

Poem for Kids

An old, old man lived down our street
as old as a tortoise with leathery feet

as old as a carp or a minstrel's harp
his eyes were dim but his wits were sharp:

he sat and watched the years go by
(perhaps he just *forgot* to die):

he sat and watched the suns go down
no one remembered when his hair was brown

(perhaps it was already white
when Waterloo men went to fight;

perhaps it was as white as frost
when Flodden field was won and lost).

I used to think he was as old
as the first drinking cups of gold

but his memories lay where they were stored
and he loved the world and he never got bored

and every night when he sank to rest
his dreams were rich, his dreams were blest.

I sometimes wondered why he seemed
so glad with whatever it was he dreamed,

and I asked him once, what his dreams were made of?
he answered, *Nothing to be afraid of:*

just memories of long-gone days
when the world moved in different ways,

just memories of things long gone:
they have passed, but I live on,

and so in the dreams inside my head
they will have a home till I am dead.

And I asked him once if he'd rather be
back when the world moved differently:

I asked him once, but all he would say
was, *Some things go and some things stay,*
and the world is a new world every day.

*

This old man had worked on a ship
and watched the billows swing and skip

in days when ships held out their sails
to catch the breezes, to dare the gales,

when the engine-room was the windy sky
and the ship drove on with her mast held high

or the ship stood still and the sails hung idle
and skipper and mate were suicidal

till the first sail swelled and the first rope stirred
and the ship came alive like a waking bird;

and there was no coal and there was no oil
just the wind and compass and seamen's toil

and there was no stain and there was no scum
in the harbours where the cargoes come

no dead birds with useless wings
washed up by the tide like forgotten things

only the shove of the salt-sea air
and the cold white horses galloping there.

And I often wondered if he longed to be
afloat again on that sparkling sea

back in those clean and salty days
before the slicks and the greasy haze:

I asked him once, but all he would say
was, *Some things go and some things stay,
and the world is a new world every day.*

*

Then one day, just before he died,
he took my arm, drew me aside:

yes, just before his spirit passed
he must have thought he'd talk at last.

*When I was born I don't remember
but from January to December*

*in every year that has gone round
since the first man walked on the ground*

things were that should never have been
and sights you'd rather not have seen.

No words can ever tell man's story
without some shame, without some glory:

if you go back a thousand years
the picture neither clouds nor clears.

Our kindly earth was not so spoiled,
yet some men lazed, and some men toiled:

some men laughed and some men groaned
and one looked on while another was stoned:

yet there was goodness, too, and boldness,
to set against the greed and coldness.

It's one long tale, without a sequel
and its bad and its good are just about equal:

so what I have to say, young man,
is, Laugh and sing as much as you can:

for some things go, and some things stay,
and the world is a new world every day!

JOHN WAIN

The Peacock and the Man from Mars

'Unique bird!'
exclaimed the Man from Mars
as he stepped from his planet car
and observed
his first peacock strutting across a lawn
with his tail feathers fanned.
    'Your beauty can hardly be borne.
In my country we have only sand-
crawlers, crater-snipes and crows.
Of peacocks we have never heard.'
    The Peacock at first rose
to the flattery
parading backwards and forwards
until this disturbing thought occurred:
    'Suppose
this Man from Mars
carries me away,
lands me in a burnt-out battery
of defunct stars?
What can I do to cover up my display?
What can I say?'
    He brought his showing-off to a halt,
folded his tail away
and declared:
    'Strange man, you must not let yourself be snared
by a beauty which is at fault.
Why, among us my wife, who is sombre,
is accounted far more beautiful than I.
And as to sparrows,

they are the most beautiful of all:
compact, colourless and small . . .
I assure you this is a taste that grows.'
   The Man from Mars did not reply
but there was a glint in his eye
and he fixed the Peacock with a look that glowed.
   'Do not be misled, sir,'
went on the Peacock with a note of fear,
'this tail means nothing to us here.
Forget what you thought you saw.
One might almost call it a flaw.'
   This self-denigration came too late.
The Man from Mars
shot out a tendrily arm and swept him towards his car's
door.
   'You are right,'
he said. 'Beauty is only something in the eye,
some gaze that inspires.
It is visual delight.
What a happy fate that we have met!
Each can give and each can get
what he least values or most desires.'
   As he tugged at a tail quill
he added:
'I expect
you find these faulty,
and also those blue-and-green feathers
with which your neck
is padded.
They'll do for my window-sill.
You can have this strap
of mine, which *I* find paltry.'
   The protests of the Peacock were shrill,
but the Man from Mars did not stop stripping him until

he was as bald as a marrow.
   'There now,'
he said stepping back
into his planet car with a bow:
'you are really beautiful –
I've made you almost as small and compact as
   a sparrow.'

PAUL ROCHE

The Wise Mud-Fish

A veteran Mud-fish in a swampy lake
in the centre of central Africa
viewed with concern the dwindling water
and the gradual burning up of his domain.
For months beyond its time
the strong sun baked
the wet of the swamp into mere mire
till even the hot slime
grew hard
and began to crack into shards.

The veteran Mud-fish was sorely worried.
All swans and water-birds were gone,
not a frog tarried,
and still the drought lasted.
'Why, it's not even mud!'
the other fish gasped
as they buried deeper under the crust.
'If this dearth of rain goes on,
soon it will be dust.
Then how shall we adjust?'

To the veteran Mud-fish it was plain
that if the rains held off
it spelled death to them in the hard earth.
But he also knew of course
that many would die through panic.

So he sought to distract them and announced
    to the race:
'No amount of worrying and wishing and being frantic
will make the sweet rains wash
over our drying swamp.
What we must do is fashion
the mud into cups
to catch the rain when it comes.
Stop fussing and go to work with a passion.'

This they did,
and losing themselves in this useless occupation,
quite forgot the dangers of dying through drying;
until a few days later the rains came in floods,
gushing and romping over the swamp
and over mud-fish, mud-cups and mud.

PAUL ROCHE

Portrait

He was a cold fish:
Deeply the stillest waters
Ran beneath him
While he nibbled moonflakes
From a silver plate.

'What do I care,' he cried
'For others in this ocean?
Let it be a mirror,
And for company the chill stars dancing
Or my own reflection.'

Yes, we all admired him
As we kept our distance, all
Except one huge and hungry shadow
Leaping from the depths
Which ate him whole.

JOHN MOLE

Over the Wall

It was not a dream,
yet something dreamlike came between
the man inside his quivering bag of skin
and all the scraped and naked world,
percussive colours, swirling trees,
that now he floundered in.
He ran
over the gorse, the humped and bristling tufts
that more than once rose up and kicked
his feet wild, skittering in the air.
The bone ground banged into his ribs,
thumped borrowed breath from snarling lungs;
he rose again
and ran and ran and ran,
eyes crackling with hot salt,
heart slamming protestant,
chest pumping past the point where it must burst.
Irons of cramp screwed tighter on his calves
and thighs dragged heaving chains,
but far away, though thickening by the minute,
he heard, behind his own harsh sobs
and rusty whimperings,
the bloodshot cries of hounds.
He ran
until his body fell
broken, hugger-mugger, on the ground.
He could not move.
He might have been
a rock or mound, a fallen trunk,

dead lump of animal.
He lay
until the outraged engines of his breathing eased,
but still he could not move.
Derisive birds clawed silence and the trusty sun,
in solitary as ever,
beamed behind gold bars.
His eyes bled darkness on their blinds.
And then he heard them moving near,
the shouts and whistles, growling engines,
the open throttles of the hounds,
and nearer yet
until at last they jostled round.
They carried him on shoulders, like a coffin.
His breathing now was sweet and effortless;
eyes stayed shut. No one saw his smile
as he was borne away to freedom
from the cruel exigencies of choice.

VERNON SCANNELL

Boy Flying

Flying,
    He saw the earth flat as a plate,
    As if there were no hills, as if houses
    Were only roofs, as if the trees
    Were only the leaves that covered
    The treetops. He could see the shadows
    The clouds cast when they sailed over the fields,
    He could see the river like the silver track
    Left by a snail, and roads narrow as ribbons.

    He could not see Mickey French next door,
    In bed with a cold, nor his two sisters
    Playing 'Happy Families' as they watched
    The television. He could not see his kitten.

Flying,
    He felt the air as solid as water
    When he spread his fingers against it.
    He felt it cool against his face, he felt
    His hair whipped. He felt weightless
    As if he were hollow, he felt the sun
    Enormously bright and warm on his back,
    He felt his eyes watering. He felt
    The small, moist drops the clouds held.

    He could not feel the grass, he could not
    Feel the rough stones of the garden wall.
    He could not remember the harsh, dry bark
    Of the apple tree against his knees.

Flying,
  He could hear the wind hissing, the note
  Changed when he turned his head. He heard
  His own voice when he sang. Very faintly,
  He heard the school bus as it grumbled
  Past the church, he thought he could hear
  The voices of the people as they shouted
  In amazement when they saw him swoop and glide.

  He could not hear the birds sing, nor the chalk
  Squeak against the blackboard, nor the mower
  As it whirred along, nor the clock tick.
  He could not hear the bacon sizzle in the pan,
  He could not hear his friend calling him.

LESLIE NORRIS

Of Itzig and His Dog

To pray for the impossible,
says Itzig, is disgraceful.
I prefer, when I'm on my own,
when I'm only with my dog,
when I can't go out
because of the weather,
because of my shoes,
to talk very intimately to God.

      Itzig, they nag, why do that,
   what's the point of that?
  God never replies, surely?

Such ignorance! Am I at the Western Wall?
Am I on spacious Mount Sinai?
Is there a thornbush in this murky room?
God may never say a word,
may never even whisper, Itzig, hullo.

But when I'm talking away
to the right and to the left,
when it's raining outside,
when there's rain on the glass,
when I say please God this
and thank God that,
then God always makes, believe me,
the dog's tail wag.

Dannie Abse

'BY RUNGS OR SHAFTS OF RHYME'

Rhyme-Time

I know that poems do not have to rhyme,
And yet I've always liked to hear words chime.
I've noticed, too, that in the world's design
Rhymes play their part, occurring all the time,
Not just in sounds but in the way the fine
Gestures of a tiny plant will mime
In miniature the flourish of a pine,
Proud and lonely on the hill's skyline;
Or how the bright refulgence of moonshine
Is almost echoed in the sheen of lime;
The way the hawthorn foams, a paradigm
For spindrift blossom on the dancing brine.
Oh yes, it's true, all poems do not rhyme
But of the things that I will treasure, nine
Times out of ten, the sounds and objects sign
Themselves on memory and warmly twine
Around the heart and rhythms of the spine
Through using chime and echo.
                                                It's no crime –
As verbal savages in grime and slime
Of their poetic darkness whine – to climb
To transcendental heights or try to mine
Deep in mysteries equally sublime
By rungs or shafts of rhyme. I know that I'm
Old fashioned but I'd never care to sign
A contract that debars the chiming line.
Finally, I ask, what sweeter rhyme
Than your close heartbeat keeping time with mine?

VERNON SCANNELL

The Quarrel

My nostrils are narrowing,
your eyes are staring,
it's terribly harrowing,
there's shouting and swearing,
the bad words are arrowing
to hurting and hearing!

My patience is going,
your anger's increasing,
your glances are glowing,
there's noise without ceasing,
a stormcock is crowing
a storm of releasing!

My fury is creaming,
no thought of the neighbours
restrains your high screaming,
it's childbirth and labours,
a nightmare we're dreaming –
but sharper than sabres!

GAVIN EWART

The Cricket

The cricket, like a knuckled rubber-band,
Whirrs from the launching platform of my hand
Without much notion where he's going to land.

But does he mind the jump or the surprise?
Suppose we chanced to be each other's size?
I know I wouldn't stay. I'd close my eyes

And jump. Are bodies chosen with a pin?
My own seems suitable for being in,
But why pale pink, rather than pale green skin?

And does some giant, wishing me no harm,
Peruse me, perfect, on his unseen palm?
What creatures stir upon the cricket's arm?

The worlds are gears upon the wheels of chance.
The worlds retreat and worlds in worlds advance.
The creatures dance. And lead themselves a dance.

Leaping the grasses like a leafy lancer,
The cricket does not know that he's a dancer.
I ask the questions, but he *is* the answer

And all the summer's day he needn't think
But simply jump, a jointed tiddlewink,
A perfect alpha minus in green ink.

JOHN FULLER

Sunday Tiger

At the road work's halt we all lean out
Of week-end cars, to point and shout

At that great beast, Blake never saw,
A length of tiger with sheathed claw,

Padding his cage of fearful symmetry,
That's parked on Clapham mud, for all to see

How living, well groomed props of circus acts
Can turn our emblems into facts.

The lights turn green. The motors start.
I pace the confines of my heart.

SHIRLEY TOULSON

Note: William Blake wrote *The Tyger* without having seen one. The animal was introduced to England at a later date.

Cat on a Wall

Nothing's more natural than a garden wall
   To rest upon, a plinth for watchful eyes;
When I am lying down it makes me tall,
   Status conferred, my place to supervise.

My master raised its courses brick by brick
   To keep him in; I claim extensive rights
Which trowel and mortar have no power to check:
   I vault across it, or command its heights.

Its shadow shrinks one side, grows on the other;
   The sun creeps on my coat; I watch shrubs' shade
For small fur, scan all the sky for feather
   Or doze to cut and thrust of master's spade.

   He built the wall, and yet he lets it be;
   He gives me milk, but I own more than he.

PAUL HYLAND

Farm Cat

Silly to say that butter would not melt
   In my mouth, for it would. But I am hard.
For all the rolls of fat beneath my pelt
   My quickness feeds me, it's my life and lard.

I am the one the farmer did not drown;
   While dogs sleep indoors, at his beck and call,
I prowl for rats in out-house and in barn,
   My comrade and competitor, the owl.

Dogs need a whistling master; I'm my own,
   And just for fun I flush sheep stealthily
From the lush ewe-leaze up on to the down;
   Soft beasts that understand my mastery.

   I'm soft as spring-water, as sharp as ice,
   And my dreams flock with huge compliant mice.

PAUL HYLAND

Night Cat

I am a Queen of cats, a paragon
  Of all the feline virtues, sleek, soft, mild,
  But quick to pounce on prey, and justly wild
When the deep night is swollen with full moon.

When fawning Toms caper about my door
  And call me, court me with their solemn cries;
  I preen, and sleep, and preen and feign surprise
Savouring passion's stench upon the air.

The air is full of fight, my feline pride
  Unsatisfied till work of tongue and paw
  Is all dishevelled by his tooth and claw:
Our eyes glint like green moons, the moon wide-eyed.

  Pale faces scowl from windows up above;
  They love no squalls, nor those who squall in love.

PAUL HYLAND

Knock Knock

(*For Ben*)

Knock Knock
Who's there?
Love
Love who?
Love you

Knock Knock
What next?
Time
Time when?
Time then

Knock Knock
Now what?
Me
Me where?
You there

Knock Knock
Who? Who?
Bones
Bones who?
Bones you

JOHN MOLE

Index of Poets

Index of Titles